Owl suggests an adventure.

Hooray, hooray! On our way!

"Hello, flutter-friend!"

Piglet finds a fluttery bush.

Oh, me, oh, my!

Small Piglet, big, big wind!

Draw a kite string from Pooh's hand to the kite.

"If there's a cloud, it finds me."

What a friendly little shower!

"Hello, long-ears!"

"Hello, buddy ol' pal!"

"Are you home, Rabbit?"

"Good morning!"

"Yum-yum! Honey for the tummy!"

Pooh is a tubby bear!

"You are the Best Bear in All the World."

"Christopher Robin, come quick!"

Roo is up in a tree.

"We'll catch you!"

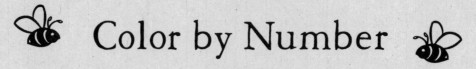

Color by Number

1: blue	3: green	5: purple
2: yellow	4: red	6: orange

It's so much friendlier with two.

Pooh has a nice, big mirror.
Which is Pooh's mirror image?

A

B

C

Your Answer: _____

Isn't it funny how a bear likes honey?

Oh dear, oh dearie, dearie dear!"

Tiggers are very down-to-earth.

Rum-tum-tiddle-um-tum!

Boing! Boing! March!

Round and round we go!

Happy, happy day!

A snooze for two.

Piglet is giggly over missing his middle.
Connect the dots to finish Piglet.

"I shall tell you a story. . .

. . .about a boy and his bear."

Tigger bounces through the Hundred-Acre Wood.

"Who wants to play hide-and-seek?"

"Hello, swishy friend!"

Pooh is a helpful bear.

Eeyore fixes his house. . . again.

Even Eeyore can be silly.

Oopsy-daisy!
Study these two pages.

Topsy-turvy!
Circle 5 things that have
been added to this picture.

"Oh, bother!"

Rain, rain, come and play!

Look at the picture and these 5 pieces.
Which 3 pieces complete the picture?

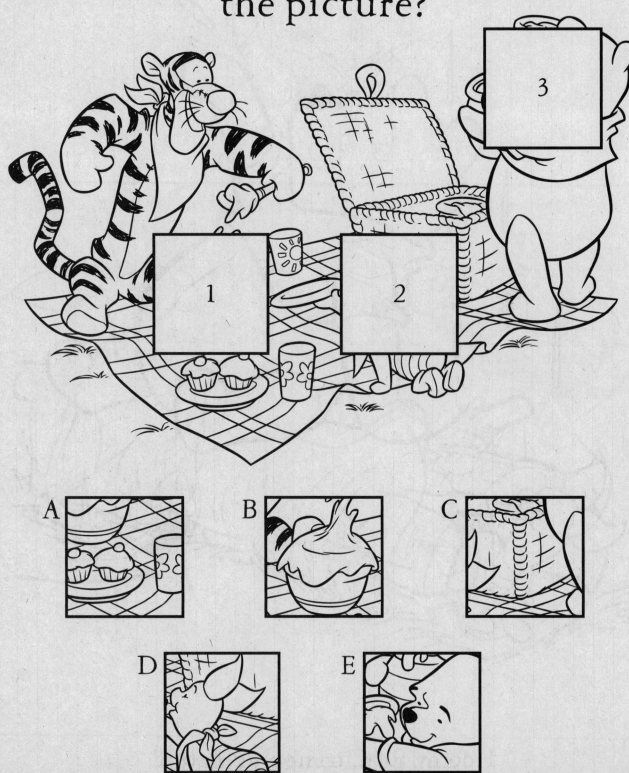

Hooray for Christopher Robin!

A hug is the best gift.

Snuggle up!

Rumbly tumblies love honey!

Winnie the Pooh is a happy bear.

How many honeypots do you count?

YOUR
ANSWER:

"Oh, my. There's a rumbly in my tumbly."

Pooh keeps his favorite food handy.

Honey!

Christopher Robin loves Winnie the Pooh.

Pooh and Piglet are best friends.

Life is simple in the Hundred-Acre Wood.

Help Pooh and Piglet find their way to Pooh Sticks Bridge.

Start

Finish

"This way, Piglet."

What a sweet surprise!

Make a wish!

Teamwork makes a job more fun.

Tigger bounces in.

Draw lines from each character to his name.

Pooh   Tigger   Piglet

Bears love honey—and so do bees.

Which bee line leads to Pooh's nose?

A

B

C

Your Answer:____

Rabbit lives in the Hundred-Acre Wood.

How many carrots do you count?

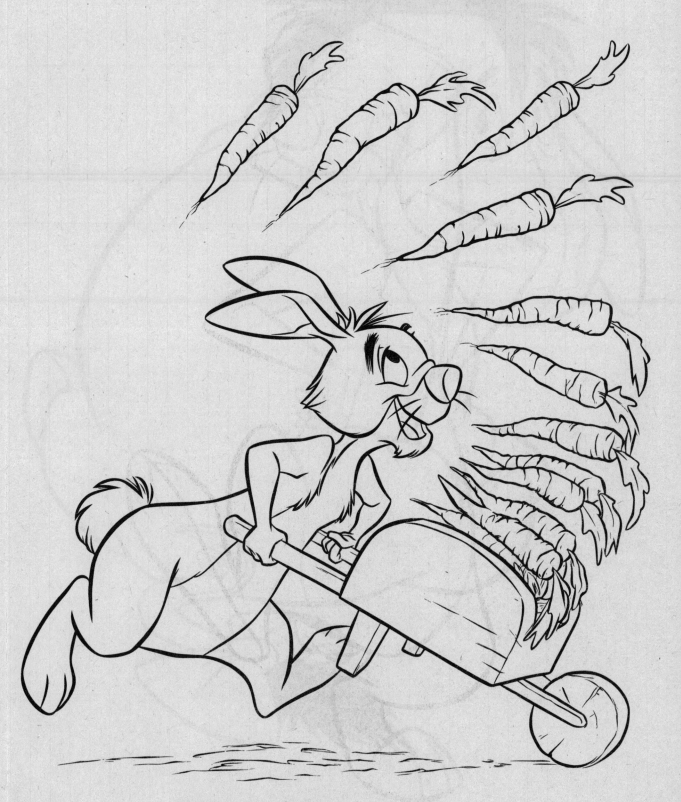

Your Answer:_____

Eeyore can be rather gloomy.

Christopher Robin fixes Eeyore's tail. . . again.

Owl likes to give advice.

Tea with honey is a nice treat.

Kanga is Roo's mother.

How many hops does Roo take to reach Kanga?

Your Answer: _____

A gift from Rabbit.

Eeyore brings a box.

Owl flies in with a present.

Roo helps Kanga.

Boing-boing-boing!

Small Piglet, big box!

What could Pooh's gift be?

Happy, Happy Day!

Look up, down, across, and diagonally
to find these words.

party   box   hats
gift   happy   yay
present   bows

P R E S E N T

P A W I M A F

I O R B O X I

B J S T A H G

H A P P Y A Y

Bear. . . balloon. . .

. . .and bees!

Pooh has a drifty day.

"Hello, little friend."

Hold on, Piglet!

Wheeeee!

It looks like rain.

Drip-drop!

An umbrella can be a little tent. . .

. . .or a floaty boat.

Think, think, think!
Draw what Pooh is thinking about.

Up, up, up!

Down, down, down!

Think, think, think!
Draw what Pooh is looking at.

What fun mud can be!